Nesting Neighbors

by Jennifer Patrick

GW00865877

To my family, my nest
R.P., C.P., and S.P.

No part of this publication may be reproduced in whole or in part, stored in a retrieval system, or transmitted in any form or by any means, electronic, mechanical, photocopying, recording, or otherwise, without prior written permission of the publisher. For information regarding permission, write to the publisher, Storybook Genius, at: 219 Jackson Street, Augusta, Missouri 63332 or visit them at www.sbgpublishing.com ISBN 978-1-949522-38-9
Text copyright© 2019 by Jennifer Patrick Illustrations copyright© 2019 by Jennifer Patrick. All rights reserved.

Published by Storybook Genius, LLC. Printed in the U.S.A

STORYBOOK
GENIUS PUBLISHING
sbgpublishing.com

Book
Design by
yipjar.com

One warm spring day, my family noticed something. We noticed another family building a home right next to ours!

It wasn't a house made from bricks, stone, or wood.
It was a home made from twigs, mud, and grass.

A mama robin had chosen the big
tree right next to our front door
to build a **nest** for her eggs!

My mom and dad were able to
quickly peek in to see the progress.
My brother and I had to be lifted.

A few days later, we noticed three bright **blue eggs**!

Robin's egg blue, to be exact!

We never got too close or touched the eggs.

Sometimes the mama bird would fly away when we were near.

Sometimes she stayed in the nest. She would quietly watch to make sure there was no danger.

One time, she even stayed snuggled in when a storm swirled around her and wind bent the tree branches.

It seemed to take forever

for the eggs to begin

hatching,

but it was only about

two weeks.

the robins!

Then it took two full
days for all of the small
pink birds to emerge.

One morning my mom noticed one pink baby bird and two eggs.

That afternoon she noticed two pink babies and one egg.

The very next day she noticed three pink babies!

The new baby birds were sure hungry! We watched the daddy bird guard the nest while the mama bird gathered food.

Sometimes we saw the daddy bird bringing worms back to the nest to feed the babies and the mama.

The bird parents worked day and night to care for their new hatchlings.

We wondered if there was anything we could do to help?
We read about things that robin birds might like to eat.

We offered some berries on a plate.
We left the plate on the ground near the tree.
The mama was not interested.

What if we found some squiggly worms for the birds?

My brother and I were up for the task, but my mom got a funny look on her face.

We decided to just **watch and learn** more about our interesting neighbors.

Each day, the birds got bigger and fluffier.

They also started **squawking** for food.

All three birds craned their necks with their mouths

open until a tasty morsel was dropped in.

We thought they might leave the nest soon

and start to fly on their own. My brother and

I wanted to name them before they left.

We decided on **Feather,**
Branch, and **Twig**

The birds practiced flying by sitting on the side of their nest and **flapping** their wings. They would beat their wings quickly but were not quite ready to take off.

Finally, after days of practicing, the babies **were** ready to take flight!

One by one, the babies left the nest.

Then mama and daddy robin flew away, too.

We were sad to see our neighbors go, but we

knew they were ready for new adventures.

Part of their nest is still there. Mom said we could clear it away because robins rarely use the same nest again, although they do sometimes come back to the same tree to lay their next eggs. I sure hope so. Spring is coming soon and they make great neighbors.

Have you ever noticed or watched
the birds near where you live?
Do you ever wonder where their nest is?
I notice the birds in my neighborhood,
now more than ever. I often wonder if any
of the robins I see are the ones from the nest.

My brother and I wrote a
song in case the birds return.
We will sing it softly to them...

"Robins, robins build your nest.
We have a tree that is best.
We'll be kind–don't you know.
We just want to watch you grow!"

Lightning Source UK Ltd.
Milton Keynes UK
UKHW050743090421
381704UK00005B/37